M000316781

# Multi-Lingual Phrase Passport

# Contents

# Intention of this Guide

This guide—*Multi-Lingual Phrase Passport* is intended to provide information useful to people living with food allergies and specialized diets. AllergyFree Passport™, LLC as the authors and R & R Publishing, LLC as the publisher (collectively "we") have made reasonable efforts to make sure that the information provided is accurate and complete. We believe that factual information contained in this guide was correct to the best of our knowledge at the time of publication. However, we do not warrant or guarantee that any of the information is accurate or complete.

We assume no responsibility for errors, inaccuracies, omissions or typographical errors contained in this guide. We expressly disclaim responsibility for any adverse effects arising from the use or application of the information contained herein, as well as responsibility for any liability, injury, loss or damage, whether it be actual, special, consequential, personal or otherwise, which is incurred or allegedly incurred as a direct or indirect consequence of the use and application of any of the contents of this guide or for references made within it.

The information contained in this guide should not be viewed as medical advice. Questions regarding specific food allergies, specialized diets, drug and food interactions and anything related to a specific individual should be addressed to a doctor or other medical practitioner.

*"If I have helped just one person in exploring
a new location, be it in the city or country side,
within their own country and/or on foreign lands,
I will feel as though I have succeeded."*
—Ralph Waldo Emerson

# Passport Introduction

## Overview

As part of the *Let's Eat Out!* series, the *Multi-Lingual Phrase Passport* is the first pocket-size phrase guide dedicated to communicating special dietary needs when eating outside the home while managing 10 common food allergens including: corn, dairy, eggs, fish, gluten, peanuts, shellfish, soy, tree nuts and wheat. This pioneering effort provides a total of  1200-plus phrases in four languages including French, German, Italian and Spanish. The contents of this passport are based on years of personal experience, extensive research, proven results and the collaborative efforts of many individuals and organizations around the world. This light-weight passport is designed to facilitate safe eating experiences in foreign language speaking countries around the world.

## Passport Approach

The passport is organized in a manner that allows you to use the information in a number of different ways. One of our key guiding principles was to develop an easy-to-use guide that is succinct and flexible to meet an individual's needs. It can be referenced by language, type of phrase required and respective allergen considerations —whatever you are most interested in communicating. Even if you do not know how to pronounce these words, the format is designed so that you may refer to these phrases when scanning a menu or point directly to the passport to express your request while in a foreign language speaking country. It's all about your needs, preferences and areas of concern during that particular moment of the day.

## Design and Methodology

The format is standardized across the four languages allowing you, the reader, to easily recognize each section of information. The *Multi-Lingual Phrase Passport* provides over 1200 phrases integral to international travel while managing specialized diets. Each phrase has been translated into French, German, Italian and Spanish by a professional technical translation service. Quality assurance testing was conducted with native speakers of each language to ensure phrase accuracy and applicability based upon contemporary cultural idioms.

These essential multi-lingual phrases represent five categories of information which you may want to communicate to hospitality resources or health professionals in restaurants, hotels or anywhere you want to convey your concerns. Relevant phrases which may be needed while eating outside the home and traveling around the globe include:

- Food allergy phrases

- Ingredient and preparation technique phrases

- Dining phrases

- Breakfast phrases

- Health and product phrases

The food allergy phrases communicate:

- Allergic conditions

- 10 common food allergens

The ingredient and preparation technique phrases detail:

- Specific ingredients by common allergen
- Preparation techniques by common allergen
- Other potential food allergens

The dining phrases communicate:

- Introductions and common courtesies
- Special requests to ensure safe dining at lunch and dinner
- Clarification questions about ingredients and food preparation

The breakfast phrases communicate:

- Breakfast meal and side dish requests
- Types of egg preparation and common ingredients
- Other breakfast items

The health phrases communicate:

- Types of health and store facilities

- Health professionals and symptoms

- Helpful products

This passport can be used as a daily resource while traveling in a foreign language speaking country, a reference guide or an educational tool depending upon your perspective. We hope it meets your diverse needs and empowers you with the knowledge to achieve your desired gluten and allergy-free objectives.

And remember,

> **"Life loves to be taken by**
> **the lapel and told,**
> **'I am with you kid. Let's go!'"**
> –Maya Angelou

*Eating is a serious venture,*
*if not a patriotic duty, in France.*
—Patricia Roberts

# French Language Translations

## Phrase Overview

The following materials outline English to French translations for:

- Food allergy phrases

- Ingredient and preparation technique phrases

- Dining phrases

- Breakfast phrases

- Health and product phrases

# French Food Allergy Phrases

The following represents a partial list of phrases needed to communicate some allergy conditions and potential allergens including:

- General allergy conditions

- 10 common food allergens

| Allergy Conditions | Conditions Allergiques |
|---|---|
| I have/am experiencing: | J'ai/je souffre: |
| an emergency | d'une situation de crise |
| anaphylactic shock | d'un choc anaphylactique |
| an allergic reaction | d'une réaction allergique |
| food allergies | d'allergies alimentaires |
| celiac/coeliac disease | de la maladie coeliaque |
| lactose intolerance | d'une intolérance au lactose |

| 10 Common Allergens | 10 Allergènes Répandus |
|---|---|
| I am allergic/ intolerant/ hypersensitive to: | Je suis allergique/ je ne tolère pas/ je suis hypersensible: |
| corn | au maïs |
| dairy | aux laitages |
| eggs | aux œufs |

| 10 Common Allergens | 10 Allergènes Répandus |
|---|---|
| fish | au poisson |
| gluten | au gluten |
| milk | au lait |
| nuts | aux noix |
| peanuts | aux cacahuètes/arachides |
| shellfish | aux mollusques et crustacés |
| soy | au soja |
| wheat | au blé |

# French Ingredient and Preparation Technique Phrases

The following represents a partial list of phrases needed to inquire about the specific cuisines and preparation considerations including:

- Key ingredients by the 10 common food allergens

- Food preparation techniques by the 10 common food allergens

- Other potential food allergens

## Key Cuisine Codes by Allergen

| Corn | Maïs |
|---|---|
| almond extract | extrait d'amandes |
| artificial bacon bits | succédanés de miettes de bacon |
| artificial mashed potato mix | purée industrielle de pommes de terre |
| batter | pâte à frire |
| bouillon | bouillon |
| bread or bread crumbs | pain ou miettes de pain |
| breading | chapelure |
| cheese | fromage |
| colors or flavors | colorants ou arômes artificiels |
| corn flour or corn meal | farine ou semoule de maïs |
| corn starch | fécule de maïs |
| corn syrup | sirop de maïs |
| imitation crab meat or seafood | succédané de chair de crabe ou fruits de mer |
| malt | malt |
| masa | masa (pâte pour tortillas) |
| salad dressing | sauce pour salade |
| sauce, dipping sauce or salsa | sauce, sauce pour trempettes, ou sauce salsa |
| seasonings | assaisonnements |

## Corn

side dishes or
   accompaniments
tortillas or tortilla
   chips
vanilla extract
vegetable oil

## Maïs

plats d'accompagnement

tortillas ou croustilles
   de maïs
extrait de vanille
huile végétale

## Dairy

artificial mashed
   potato mix
bread or bread crumbs
breading
butter
cakes or cookies
cheese or blue cheese
chocolate
colors or flavors

cream, sour cream
   whipped cream
milk or buttermilk
sauce or dipping sauce

seasonings

## Laitages

purée industrielle de
   pommes de terre
pain et miettes de pain
chapelure
beurre
gâteaux ou biscuits
fromage ou bleu
chocolat
colorants ou arômes
   artificiels
crème, crème aigre ou or
   crème fouettée
blait ou babeurre
sauce ou sauce pour
   trempettes
assaisonnements

### Dairy

side dishes or
  accompaniments

yogurt, yogurt curd
  or yogurt sauce

### Laitages

plats d'accompagnement

yogourt, caillé ou sauce
  au yogourt

### Eggs

batter

bread or bread crumbs

breading

cakes or cookies

croutons

custard

dumpling skin

egg sealer

egg yolk

imitation crab meat
  or seafood

mayonnaise

noodles or pasta

salad dressing

sauce or dipping sauce

side dishes or
  accompaniments

### Œufs

pâte à frire

pain ou miettes de pain

chapelure

gâteaux ou biscuits

croûtons

crème pâtissière

couverture de pâte

scellement blanc d'œuf

jaune d'œuf

succédané de chair de
  crabe ou fruits de mer

mayonnaise

nouilles ou pâtes

sauce pour salade

sauce ou sauce pour
  trempettes

plats d'accompagnement

## Fish

anchovies
fish sauce
imitation crab meat
  or seafood
salad dressing
salmon
stock or broth
tuna

## Gluten/Wheat

artificial bacon bits

artificial mashed potato
  mix
batter
beans
bouillon
bread or bread crumbs
breading
cakes or cookies
cheese or blue cheese
colors or flavors

croutons
dedicated fryer

## Poisson

anchois
sauce de poisson (nuoc mâm)
succédané de chair de
  crabe ou fruits de mer
sauce pour salade
saumon
fond ou consommé
thon

## Gluten/Blé

succédanés de miettes de
  bacon
purée industrielle de
  pommes de terre
pâte à frire
haricots
bouillon
pain ou miettes de pain
chapelure
gâteaux ou biscuits
fromage ou bleu
colorants ou arômes
  artificiels
croûtons
friteuse specifique

| Gluten/Wheat | Gluten/Blé |
|---|---|
| dumpling skin | couverture de pâte |
| fish sauce | sauce de poisson (nuoc mâm) |
| flour dusting | saupoudrage de farine |
| fluffing agent | agent de levage |
| fresh oil | huile fraîche |
| imitation crab meat or seafood | succédané de chair de crabe ou fruits de mer |
| malt | malt |
| malt vinegar | vinaigre de malt |
| marinade | marinade |
| noodles or pasta | nouilles ou pâtes |
| salad dressing | sauce pour salade |
| sauce, dipping sauce or salsa | sauce, sauce pour trempettes, ou sauce salsa |
| seasonings | assaisonnements |
| side dishes or accompaniments | plats d'accompagnement |
| soy sauce | sauce au soja |
| stabilizers | agent stabilisant |
| thickening agent | agent épaississant |
| tortillas or tortilla chips | tortillas ou croustilles de maïs |
| wheat flour | farine de blé |
| yogurt, yogurt curd or yogurt sauce | yogourt, caillé ou sauce au yogourt |

## Peanuts

bread or bread crumbs
cakes or cookies
colors or flavors

garnishes
peanut oil
sauce or dipping sauce

side dishes or
    accompaniments
vegetable bisque
vegetable oil

## Shellfish

calamari
crab
escargot (snails)
lobster
mussels
oysters
shrimp
stock or broth

## Cacahuètes/Arachides

pain ou miettes de pain
gâteaux ou biscuits
colorants ou arômes
    artificiels
garnitures
huile d'arachide
sauce ou sauce pour
    trempettes
plats d'accompagnement

bisque de légumes
huile végétale

## Mollusques et Crustacés

calamars
crabe
escargots
homard
moules
huitres
crevettes
fond ou consommé

| Soy | Soja |
|---|---|
| artificial bacon bits | succédanés de miettes de bacon |
| artificial mashed potato mix | purée industrielle de pommes de terre |
| bean curd | caillé de soja (tofu) |
| bouillon | bouillon |
| bread or bread crumbs | pain ou miettes de pain |
| breading | chapelure |
| cheese | fromage |
| chocolate | chocolat |
| colors or flavors | colorants ou arômes artificiels |
| imitation crab meat or seafood | succédané de chair de crabe ou fruits de mer |
| ketchup | ketchup |
| masa | masa |
| mayonnaise | mayonnaise |
| salad dressing | sauce pour salade |
| sauce, dipping sauce or salsa | sauce, sauce pour trempettes, ou sauce salsa |
| seasonings | assaisonnements |
| side dishes or accompaniments | plats d'accompagnement |
| soy sauce | sauce au soja |
| tofu | tofu |

| | |
|---|---|
| tortillas or tortilla chips | tortillas ou croustilles de maïs |
| vegetable oil | huile végétale |
| yogurt, yogurt curd or yogurt sauce | yogourt, caillé ou sauce au yogourt |

## Tree Nuts

## Noix autres que l'Arachide

| | |
|---|---|
| almonds or almond extract | amandes ou extrait d'amandes |
| bread or bread crumbs | pain ou miettes de pain |
| cakes or cookies | gâteaux ou biscuits |
| colors or flavors | colorants ou arômes artificiels |
| cashews or cashew powder | noix de cajou ou cajou en poudre |
| garnishes | garnitures |
| pistachios | pistaches |
| sauce, dipping sauce or salsa | sauce, sauce pour trempettes, ou sauce salsa |
| side dishes or accompaniments | plats d'accompagnement |
| vegetable bisque | bisque de légumes |
| walnuts | noix |

## Other Potential Food Allergens

## Autres Allergènes Alimentaires Potentiels

I am allergic/
intolerant/
hypersensitive to:

Je suis allergique/
je ne tolère pas/
je suis hypersensible

- aspartame
- bacon
- dyes
- fructose
- garlic
- ham
- monosodium glutamate

- onions
- pork
- preservatives
- rice
- sodium nitrate
- vegetable starch
- vinegar
- yeast

à l'aspartame
au bacon
aux colorants
au fructose
à l'ail
au jambon
au glutamate
    monosodique

aux oignons
au porc
aux conservateurs
au riz
au nitrate de sodium
à l'amidon végétal
au vinaigre
à la levure

# French Dining Phrases

The following represents relevant phrases needed to communicate special dietary considerations to chefs and servers in restaurants around the globe and include:

- Introductions and common courtesies
- Special requests to ensure safe dining
- Clarification questions to ensure against cross contamination

## Introductions

Hello. I'm sorry, but I do not speak French.

I need to special order my meal due to my food allergies.

I am on a medically prescribed allergy-free diet.

I need your assistance.

Thank you for your help.

I cannot eat these foods because I will become ill.

## Introductions

Bonjour, je suis désolé(e), mais je ne parle pas français.

J'ai besoin d'une commande spéciale pour mon repas car j'ai des allergies alimentaires.

Je suis sur un régime médical évitant les aliments allergènes.

J'ai besoin de votre aide.

Merci pour votre aide.

Je ne peux pas manger ces aliments parce que ça me rendrait malade.

### Introductions

I have a condition called
celiac/coeliac disease.

I cannot eat the smallest
amount of gluten which is
wheat, rye or barley.

### Introductions

Je souffre de la maladie
coeliaque.

Je ne peux pas absorber
la moindre quantité de
gluten, qu'il provienne du
blé, du seigle ou de l'orge.

### Foods That I Can Eat

I can eat:
  all kinds of fruit
  meat
  potatoes
  rice
  fresh stocks and broths

  all kinds of vegetables
  wine based vinegars
  distilled vinegar
  rice flour or gluten-free
    noodles
  sauce with butter, eggs,
    vegetables, olive oil,
    tomatoes, herbs

### Les Aliments que Je Peux Consommer

Je peux manger:
  toutes sortes de fruits
  de la viande
  des pommes de terre
  du riz
  des bouillons frais
    et des consommés
  toutes sortes de légumes
  des vinaigres de vin
  de vinaigre distill
  de la farine de riz ou
    des pâtes sans gluten
de la sauce avec du beurre,
  des œufs, des légumes,
  l'huile d'olives, des
  tomates, des herbes

## Foods That I Can Eat

I prefer food that is:
- broiled
- grilled
- pan fried
- roasted
- steamed

Could you suggest a few menu items that are safe for me to eat with my allergies?

## Special Food Requests

Please:
- salad dressing on the side
- sauce on the side
- plain

No:
- bread
- breading
- bread crumbs

## Les Aliments que Je Peux Consommer

Je préfère les plats qui sont:
- grillés
- grillés
- sautés à la poêle
- rôtis
- cuits à la vapeur

Pouvez-vous me suggérer quelques plats du menu qui soient sans danger pour moi compte tenu de mes allergies ?

## Demandes Alimentaires Spéciales

S'il vous plait je voudrais:
- de la sauce de salade servie à part
- la sauce servie à part
- nature

Non merci je ne prends pas:
- de pain
- de chapelure
- de miettes de pain

## Special Food Requests

| | |
|---|---|
| butter | de beurre |
| chocolate | de chocolat |
| corn starch | d'amidon |
| cream | de crème |
| croutons | de croûtons |
| ketchup | de ketchup |
| mayonnaise | de mayonnaise |
| pasta | de pâtes |
| peanut oil | d'huile d'arachide |
| salad dressing | de sauce pour salade |
| soy sauce | de sauce au soja |
| vegetable oil | d'huile végétale |
| corn tortilla | de tortilla de maïs |
| wheat flour tortilla | de tortilla à la farine de blé |

## Demandes Alimentaires Spéciales

No dish with wheat flour in the:

batter
bouillon
meat/fish dusting

sauce

Pas de plat avec de la farine de blé, comme:

de la pâte à frir
du bouillon
un farinage de viande/poisson

de la sauce

Do you have wheat free soy sauce?

Avez-vous de la sauce au soja sans blé ?

## Clarification Points

If you are uncertain about what the food contains, please tell me.

Is this food dusted with wheat flour prior to cooking?

Is this food cooked on the same grill as fish/meat cooked with breading?

Is this food fried in peanut oil?

What type of garnishes are included in this dish?

What type of oil is used in the kitchen?

Is this food fried in the same fryer as items fried with breading?

Please ask the chef whether the meal I have ordered is safe for me.

## Points de Clarification

Si vous n'êtes pas sûr de ce que contiennent les plats, soyez gentil de me le dire.

Est-ce que cet aliment est fariné à la farine de blé avant d'être cuit?

Est-ce que cet aliment est cuit sur le même grill que d'autres poissons/viandes préalablement enduits de chapelure?

Cet aliment, est-il frit dans l'huile d'arachide?

Quels types de garnitures accompagnent ce plat?

Quel est le type d'huile utilisé en cuisine?

Cet aliment est-il cuit dans la même friteuse que des aliments enrobés de chapelure?

Veuillez demander au chef de cuisine si le plat que j'ai commandé est sans danger pour moi.

# French Breakfast Phrases

The following represents relevant phrases needed to communicate special dietary considerations to chefs and servers in restaurants around the globe for breakfast and include:

- Breakfast meal and side dish requests
- Types of egg preparation and common ingredients
- Other breakfast items

### Egg Dishes
eggs benedict
huevos mexicanos
huevos rancheros
skillets – american style

### Recettes à Base d'Œufs
œufs benedict
oeufs mexicanos
oeufs rancheros
œufs frits-style américain

### Eggs – Made to Order
eggs (white and yolk)
egg beaters
egg white
egg yolk

### Composition des Œufs
œufs (blanc et jaune)
blancs montés en neige
blanc d'œuf
jaune d'œuf

### Egg Preparation
boiled
fried in butter
fried in oil

### Préparation des Œufs
à la coque
frits au beurre
frits à l'huile

| Egg Preparation | Préparation des Œufs |
|---|---|
| hard boiled | durs |
| poached | pochés |
| scrambled with milk and cooked in butter | battus dans du lait et cuits au beurre |
| scrambled plain or with water and cooked in oil | brouillés nature ou détendus à l'eau et cuits à l'huile |
| soft boiled | mollets |
| sunny side up | au plat |
| yolk broken | au plat jaune brisé |

| Omelets and Potential Ingredients | Omelettes et Ingrédients Potentiels |
|---|---|
| plain | nature |
| asparagus | asperges |
| avocado | avocat |
| bacon | bacon |
| broccoli | broccoli |
| cheese | fromage |
| chicken | poulet |
| chiles | piments |
| chives | ciboulette |
| chorizo | chorizo |
| garlic | ail |
| green beans | haricots verts |

## Omelets and Potential Ingredients

| | |
|---|---|
| green pepper | poivron |
| ham | jambon |
| herbs | herbes |
| jalapenos | piment jalapeño |
| mushrooms | champignons |
| olives | olives |
| onions | oignons |
| potatoes | pommes de terre |
| red peppers | piments rouges |
| sausage – chicken | saucisse de poulet |
| sausage – pork | saucisse de porc |
| sausage – turkey | saucisse de dinde |
| spinach | épinards |
| tomatoes | tomates |

## Omelettes et Ingrédients Potentiels

## Cheese and Yogurts

| | |
|---|---|
| cheese | fromage |
| cottage cheese | fromage à tartiner |
| plain yogurt | yogourt entier |
| fruit yogurt | yogourt aux fruits |
| natural yogurt | yogourt nature |
| soy yogurt | yogourt au soja |
| soy fruit yogurt | yogourt au soja aux fruits |
| yogurt drink | yogourt à boire |

## Fromages et Yogourts

## Meat Side Dishes

bacon
canadian bacon

chorizo
corned beef hash
ham
sausage – chicken
sausage – pork
sausage – turkey
steak
turkey

## Viandes d'Accompagnement

bacon
bacon canadien (bacon
   de dos enrobé de pois)
chorizo
hachis de corned beef
jambon
saucisse de poulet
saucisse de porc
saucisse de dinde
tranche de bœuf
dinde

## From the Sea Side Dishes

lox or smoked salmon
sardines
shrimp
tuna
white fish

## Poissons d'Accompagnement

saumon fumé
sardines
crevettes
thon
poisson blanc

## Potato & Salad Side Dishes

french fries
hash browns
sautéed potatoes
mixed green salad
fruit salad

## Pommes de Terre et Salades d'Accompagnement

frites
pommes de terre rissolées
pommes de terre sautées
mesclun de salade
salade de fruits

| Fruits | Fruits |
|---|---|
| apple | pomme |
| apricot | abricot |
| banana | banane |
| berries | baies de saison |
| blueberries | myrtilles |
| blackberries | mûres |
| boysenberries | mûres de boysen |
| cantaloupe | melon |
| cherries | cerises |
| clementines | clémentines |
| cranberries | airelles rouges |
| grapes | raisin |
| grapefruit | pamplemousse |
| honey dew | melon |
| kumquat | kumquat |
| loganberries | mûres de logan |
| melon | melon |
| nectarine | nectarine |
| orange | orange |
| papaya | papaye |
| peach | pêche |
| pear | poire |
| plantain | banane plantain |
| pineapple | ananas |
| plum | prune |

## Fruits

prunes
raisins
raspberries
strawberries
tangerine

## Fruits

pruneaux
raisins secs
framboises
fraises
clémentine

## Spreads, Jams and Jellies

butter
confiture
cream cheese
honey
jams
jellies
margarine
marmalades
peanut butter
preserves

## Tartines, Confitures et Gelées

beurre
confiture
fromage à la crème
miel
confitures
gelées
margarine
marmelades
beurre de cacahuètes
conserves de fruits

## Bakery Products

bagels
biscuits
breads
buns
coffee cake

## Produits de Boulangerie/ Viennoiseries

bagels
biscuits
pains
petits pains au lait
moka

| **Bakery Products** | **Produits de Boulangerie/ Viennoiseries** |
|---|---|
| crackers | crackers |
| croissant | croissant |
| donuts | beignets |
| muffin | muffin |
| rolls | pains |
| rice cakes | gâteaux de riz |
| scones | scones |

| **Breakfast Specialties** | **Spécialités pour Petits-Déjeuners** |
|---|---|
| blintzes | blinis |
| cereal – cold | céréales froides |
| cereal – hot | céréales chaudes |
| crepes | crêpes fines |
| french toast | pain perdu |
| pancakes | crêpes |
| waffles | gaufres |
| toast | pain grillé |

| **Acceptable Gluten-Free Grains** | **Grains sans Gluten Acceptables** |
|---|---|
| amaranth | amarante |
| buckwheat | sarrasin |
| corn | maïs |
| millet | millet |
| quinoa | quinoa |
| rice | riz |

# French Health and Product Phrases

The following represents relevant phrases needed to communicate special health considerations to medical professionals and hospitality staff while traveling around the globe. The health phrases include:

- Listing of health facilities
- Listing of health professionals
- Symptoms that may need to be communicated to medical professionals
- Helpful products

| Health and Store Facilities | Magasins de Santé et Paramédicaux |
|---|---|
| I'm looking for/ need a: | Je cherche/j'ai besoin de trouver: |
| drug store | une parapharmacie |
| health food store | un magasin de produits diététiques |
| grocery store | une épicerie |
| hospital | l'hôpital |
| pharmacy | une pharmacie |

## Health Professionals

I need to see/speak
with a:

    doctor
    dietician
    nutritionist
    pediatrician
    pharmacist

## Professionnels de la Santé

J'ai besoin de
consulter/de parler à:

    un docteur
    un diététicien
    un nutritionniste
    un pédiatre
    un pharmacien

## Symptoms

I have severe/moderate:

    abdominal bloating
    abdominal cramping
    acid reflux
    asthma
    bone/joint pain

    constipation
    diarrhea
    eczema
    fatigue
    flatulence (gas)
    headaches
    hives
    migraines

## Symptômes

Je souffre de façon
sévère/modérée:

    de ballonnements
    de crampes abdominales
    de reflux acide
    d'asthme
    de douleur osseuse/
       articulaire
    de constipation
    de diarrhée
    d'eczéma
    de fatigue
    de flatulence (gaz)
    de maux de tête
    d'urticaire
    de migraines

## Symptoms

mouth ulcers
nausea
rash

seizures
sinus infection
vomiting
wheezing

## Symptômes

d'aphtes buccaux
de nausées
d'éruption cutanée
soudaine
de crises épileptiques
de sinusite
de vomissements
de respiration sifflante

## Allergen Free Products

I would like to purchase
products that are:
organic
corn-free
dairy-free
egg-free
fish-free
gluten-free
milk-free
nut-free
peanut-free
shellfish-free

soy-free
wheat-free

## Produits Non Allergènes

Je désire acheter des
produits qui soient:
organiques
sans maïs
sans laitages
sans œufs
sans poisson
sans gluten
sans lait
sans noix
sans cacahuètes
sans mollusques et
crustacés
sans soja
sans blé

| Beverages | Boissons |
|---|---|
| Do you have: | Avez-vous: |
| gingerale | du soda au gingembre |
| chamomile tea without caffeine | de la tisane camomille |
| detox tea without caffeine | de la tisane detox |
| ginger tea with caffeine | du thé au gingembre |
| ginger tea without caffeine | de la tisane au gingembre |
| green tea | du thé vert |
| peppermint tea with caffeine | du thé à la menthe |
| peppermint tea without caffeine | de la tisane à la menthe |

| Herbs/Supplements/Medicines | Herbes/Suppléments/Médecines |
|---|---|
| I am looking for: | Je cherche: |
| acid reflux medicine | un produit contre les remontées acides |
| aloe vera | de l'aloès officinal |
| analgesic ointment | de la pommade analgésique |
| antacids | des antiacides |
| antihistamine | de l'antihistaminique |
| calomine lotion | de la lotion calamine |
| charcoal | du charbon |
| dandelion root | de la racine de pissenlit |

## Herbs/Supplements/Medicines

digestive aids

digestive enzymes
epinephrine
fennel
ginger
ginger root
grapefruit seed

hydrochloric acid
itch stopping cream

milk of magnesium
peppermint
probiotics
turmeric

-to take orally
-to apply topically

## Bath

I would like to buy:
bath salt
sea salts
epsom salts

## Herbes/Suppléments/Médecines

un produit pour faciliter
la digestion
des enzymes digestives
de l'adrénaline
du fenouil
du gingembre
de la racine de gingembre
de la graine de
pamplemousse
de l'acide chlorhydrique
de la crème anti-
démangeaisons
du curcuma
la menthe
probiotics
la safran des Indes

-par voie orale
-pour application locale

## Bain

Je désire acheter:
des sels de bains
des sels marins
de l'epsomite

*The doer alone learneth.*
—Friedrich Nietzche

# German Language Translations

## Phrase Overview

The following materials outline English to German translations for:

- Food allergy phrases
- Ingredient and preparation technique phrases
- Dining phrases
- Breakfast phrases
- Health and product phrases

# German Food Allergy Phrases

The following represents a partial list of phrases needed to communicate some allergy conditions and potential allergens including:

- General allergy conditions
- 10 common food allergens

### Allergy Conditions

I have/am experiencing:
  an emergency
  anaphylactic shock
  an allergic reaction
  food allergies
  celiac/coeliac disease
  lactose intolerance

### Allergische Reaktionen

Ich habe/bin:
  einen Notfall
  anaphylaktischen Schock
  eine allergische Reaktion
  Lebensmittelallergien
  Zöliakie und Sprue
  Laktoseintoleranz

### 10 Common Allergens

I am allergic/intolerant/
hypersensitive to:

  corn
  dairy
  eggs
  fish

### 10 häufige Allergene

Ich bin allergisch/
unverträglich/
überempfindlich gegen:
  Mais
  Milchprodukte
  Eier
  Fisch

| 10 Common Allergens | 10 häufige Allergene |
|---|---|
| gluten | Gluten |
| milk | Milch |
| nuts | Nüsse |
| peanuts | Erdnüsse |
| shellfish | Schalentiere |
| soy | Soja |
| wheat | Weizen |

# German Ingredient and Preparation Technique Phrases

The following represents a partial list of phrases needed to inquire about specific cuisines and preparation considerations including:

- Key ingredients by the 10 common food allergens

- Food preparation techniques by the 10 common food allergens

- Other potential food allergens

## Key Cuisine Codes by Allergen

| Corn | Mais |
|---|---|
| almond extract | Mandelextrakt |
| artificial bacon bits | Synthetische Speckstückchen |
| artificial mashed potato mix | Synthetische Kartoffelbreimischung |
| batter | Teig |
| bouillon | Bouillon |
| bread or bread crumbs | Brot oder Semmelbrösel |
| breading | Panade |
| cheese | Käse |
| colors or flavors | Farb- oder Geschmacksstoffe |
| corn flour or corn meal | Maismehl oder Maisgrieß |
| corn starch | Maisstärke |
| corn syrup | Maissirup |
| imitation crab meat or seafood | Krabbenfleisch- oder Meeresfrüchte-Imitat |
| malt | Malz |
| masa | Masa-Maismehl |
| salad dressing | Salatsoße |
| sauce, dipping sauce or salsa | Soße, Dips oder Salsa |
| seasonings | Gewürze |
| side dishes or accompaniments | Beilagen |
| tortillas or tortilla chips | Tortillas oder Tortilla-Chips |

Corn

vanilla extract

vegetable oil

Dairy

artificial mashed potato
   mix

bread or bread crumbs

breading

butter

cakes or cookies

cheese or blue cheese

chocolate

colors or flavors

cream, sour cream or
   whipped cream

milk or buttermilk

sauce or dipping sauce

seasonings

side dishes or
   accompaniments

yogurt, yogurt curd or
   yogurt sauce

Mais

Vanilleextrakt

Pflanzenöl

Milchprodukte

Synthetische
   Kartoffelbreimischung

Brot oder Semmelbrösel

Panade

Butter

Kuchen oder Kekse

Käse oder Blauschimmelkäse

Schokolade

Farb- oder Geschmacksstoffe

Sahne, saure Sahne
   oder Schlagsahne

Milch oder Buttermilch

Soße oder Dips

Gewürze

Beilagen

Joghurt, Quark oder
   Joghurtsoße

| **Eggs** | **Eier** |
|---|---|
| batter | Teig |
| bread or bread crumbs | Brot oder Semmelbrösel |
| breading | Panade |
| cakes or cookies | Kuchen oder Kekse |
| croutons | Croutons |
| custard | Vanillepudding |
| dumpling skin | Wan-Tan-Blätter |
| egg sealer | Mit Ei verkleben |
| egg yolk | Eigelb |
| imitation crab meat or seafood | Krabbenfleisch- oder Meeresfrüchte-Imitat |
| mayonnaise | Mayonnaise |
| noodles or pasta | Pasta/Nudeln |
| salad dressing | Salatsoße |
| sauce or dipping sauce | Soße oder Dips |
| side dishes or accompaniments | Beilagen |

| **Fish** | **Fisch** |
|---|---|
| anchovies | Sardellen |
| fish sauce | Fischsoße |
| imitation crab meat or seafood | Krabbenfleisch- oder Meeresfrüchte-Imitat |
| salad dressing | Salatsoße |
| salmon | Lachs |

| | |
|---|---|
| **Fish** | **Fisch** |
| stock or broth | Brühe |
| tuna | Tunfisch |
| | |
| **Gluten/Wheat** | **Gluten/Weizen** |
| artificial bacon bits | Synthetische Speckstückchen |
| artificial mashed potato mix | Synthetische Kartoffelbreimischung |
| batter | Teig |
| beans | Bohnen |
| bouillon | Bouillon |
| bread or bread crumbs | Brot oder Semmelbrösel |
| breading | Panade |
| cakes or cookies | Kuchen oder Kekse |
| cheese or blue cheese | Käse oder Blauschimmelkäse |
| colors or flavors | Farb- oder Geschmacksstoffe |
| croutons | Croutons |
| dedicated fryer | Friteuse |
| dumpling skin | Wan-Tan-Blätter |
| fish sauce | Fischsoße |
| flour dusting | Bemehlung |
| fluffing agent | Treibmittel |
| fresh oil | Frisches Öl |
| imitation crab meat or seafood | Krabbenfleisch- oder Meeresfrüchte-Imitat |
| malt | Malz |

### Gluten/Wheat

| Gluten/Wheat | Gluten/Weizen |
|---|---|
| malt vinegar | Malzessig |
| marinade | Marinade |
| noodles or pasta | Pasta/Nudeln |
| salad dressing | Salatsoße |
| sauce, dipping sauce or salsa | Soße, Dips oder Salsa |
| seasonings | Gewürze |
| side dishes or accompaniments | Beilagen |
| soy sauce | Sojasoße |
| stabilizers | Stabilisatoren |
| thickening agent | Verdickungsmittel |
| tortillas or tortilla chips | Tortillas oder Tortilla-Chips |
| wheat flour | Weizenmehl |
| yogurt, yogurt curd or yogurt sauce | Joghurt, Quark oder Joghurtsoße |

### Peanuts

| Peanuts | Erdnüsse |
|---|---|
| bread or bread crumbs | Brot oder Semmelbrösel |
| cakes or cookies | Kuchen oder Kekse |
| colors or flavors | Farb- oder Geschmacksstoffe |
| garnishes | Garnierung |
| peanut oil | Erdnussöl |
| sauce or dipping sauce | Soße oder Dips |
| side dishes or accompaniments | Beilagen |

## Peanuts

vegetable bisque
vegetable oil

## Shellfish

calamari
crab
escargot (snails)
lobster
mussels
oysters
mussels
shrimp
stock or broth

## Soy

artificial bacon bits
artificial mashed potato
    mix
bean curd
bouillon
bread or bread crumbs
breading
cheese
chocolate
colors or flavors

## Erdnüsse

Gemüsecremesuppe
Pflanzenöl

## Schalentiere

Kalamari
Krabben
Weinbergschnecken
Hummer
Muscheln
Austern
Muscheln
Shrimps
Brühe

## Soja

Synthetische Speckstückchen
Synthetische
    Kartoffelbreimischung
Sojabohnenquark
Bouillon
Brot oder Semmelbrösel
Panade
Käse
Schokolade
Farb- oder Geschmacksstoffe

## Soy

imitation crab meat
   or seafood
ketchup
masa
mayonnaise
salad dressing
sauce, dipping sauce or salsa
seasonings
side dishes or
   accompaniments
soy sauce
tofu
tortillas or tortilla chips
vegetable oil
yogurt, yogurt curd
   or yogurt sauce

## Soja

Krabbenfleisch- oder
   Meeresfrüchte-Imitat
Ketchup
Masa-Maismehl
Mayonnaise
Salatsoße
Soße, Dips oder Salsa
Gewürze
Beilagen

Sojasoße
Tofu
Tortillas oder Tortilla-Chips
Pflanzenöl
Joghurt, Quark oder
   Joghurtsoße

## Tree Nuts

almonds or almond extract
bread or bread crumbs
cakes or cookies
colors or flavors
cashews or cashew
powder
garnishes

## Nüsse

Mandeln oder Mandelextrakt
Brot oder Semmelbrösel
Kuchen oder Kekse
Farb- oder Geschmacksstoffe
Cashews oder
gemahlene Cashews
Garnierung

| Tree Nuts | Nüsse |
|---|---|
| pistachios | Pistazien |
| sauce, dipping sauce or salsa | Soße, Dips oder Salsa |
| side dishes or accompaniments | Beilagen |
| vegetable bisque | Gemüsecremesuppe |
| walnuts | Walnüsse |

| Other Potential Food Allergens | Andere potenzielle Lebensmittelallergene |
|---|---|
| I am allergic/intolerant/ hypersensitive to: | Ich bin allergisch/ unverträglich/ überempfindlich gegen |
| aspartame | Aspartamhaltigen Süßstoff |
| bacon | Frühstücksspeck |
| dyes | Farbstoffe |
| fructose | Fruktose (Fruchtzucker) |
| garlic | Knoblauch |
| ham | Kochschinken |
| monosodium glutamate | Natriumglutamat |
| onions | Zwiebeln |
| pork | Schweinefleisch |
| preservatives | Konservierungsstoffe |
| rice | Reis |

| Other Potential Food Allergens | Andere potenzielle Lebensmittelallergene |
|---|---|
| sodium nitrate | Natriumnitrat |
| vegetable starch | Pflanzenstärke |
| vinegar | Essig |
| yeast | Hefe |

# German Dining Phrases

The following represents relevant phrases needed to communicate special dietary considerations to chefs and servers in restaurants around the globe and includes:

- Introductions and common courtesies

- Special requests to ensure safe dining

- Clarification questions to ensure against cross-contamination

### Introductions
Hello. I'm sorry, but I not speak German.

I need to special order my meal due to my food allergies.

### Einleitungen
Hallo. Ich spreche leider do kein Deutsch.

Ich muss wegen meiner Lebensmittelallergie eine Sonderbestellung aufgeben.

## Introductions

I am on a medically prescribed allergy-free diet.

I need your assistance.

Thank you for your help.

I cannot eat these foods because I will become ill.

I have a condition called celiac/coeliac disease.

I cannot eat the smallest amount of gluten which is wheat, rye or barley.

## Foods that I can eat

I can eat:

    all kinds of fruit

    meat

    potatoes

    rice

    fresh stocks and broths

    all kinds of vegetables

    wine based vinegars

    distilled vinegar

## Einleitungen

Mir wurde vom Arzt eine allergenfreie Diät vorgeschrieben.

Ich brauche Ihre Hilfe.

Danke für Ihre Hilfe.

Ich darf diese Lebensmittel nicht essen, weil ich davon krank werde.

Ich leide unter Zöliakie und Sprue.

Ich darf keinerlei Gluten zu mir nehmen. Gluten sind im Weizen, Roggen und Gerste enthalten.

## Lebensmittel, die ich essen darf

Ich darf essen:

    jedes Obst

    Fleisch

    Kartoffeln

    Reis

    frische Brühe und Bouillon

    jedes Gemüse

    Weinessige

    Branntweinessig

### Foods that I can eat

rice flour or gluten-free
    noodles
sauce with butter, eggs,
    vegetables, olive oil,
    tomatoes, herbs

I prefer food that is:
    broiled
    grilled
    pan fried
    roasted
    steamed

Could you suggest a few
menu items that are
safe for me to eat with
my allergies?

### Special Food Requests

Please:
    sauce on the side
    plain

### Lebensmittel, die ich essen darf

Reismehl oder
    glutenfreie Nudeln
Soße aus Butter, Eiern,
    Gemüse, Olivenöl,
    Tomaten, Kräutern

Ich möchte mein Essen:
    gebraten
    gegrillt
    kurzgebraten
    geschmort
    gedämpft

Können Sie mir einige
Gerichte empfehlen, die
trotz meiner Allergie
für mich geeignet sind?

### Sonderwünsche bei der Bestellung im Restaurant

Bitte:
    Soße auf einem Extrateller
    keine Soße

## Special Food Requests

No:

bread
breading
bread crumbs
butter
chocolate
corn starch
cream
croutons
ketchup
mayonnaise
pasta
peanut oil
salad dressing
soy sauce
vegetable oil
corn tortilla
wheat flour tortilla

## Sonderwünsche bei der Bestellung im Restaurant

Kein/e:

Brot
Panade
Semmelbrösel
Butter
Schokolade
Maisstärke
Sahne
Croutons
Ketchup
Mayonnaise
Pasta
Erdnussöl
Salatsoße
Sojasoße
Pflanzenöl
Maistortilla
Weizenmehltortilla

## Special Food Requests

No dish with wheat flour
in the:

    batter

    bouillon

    meat/fish dusting


    sauce

Do you have wheat-free
soy sauce?

## Clarification Points

If you are uncertain
about what the food
contains, please tell me.

Is this food dusted with
wheat flour prior to cooking?

Is this food cooked on
the same grill as fish/meat
cooked with breading?

Is this food fried in
peanut oil?

## Sonderwünsche bei der Bestellung im Restaurant

Kein Gericht mit
Weizenmehl in/an der/dem:

    Teig

    Bouillon

    Fleisch/Fisch mit
      Wizenmehl

    Soße

Haben Sie weizenfreie
Sojasoße?

## Klarstellungspunkte

Wenn Sie nicht sicher
sind, was das jeweilige
Lebensmittel enthält,
sagen Sie es mir bitte.

Wird dieses Lebensmittel
vor dem Kochen mit
Weizenmehl bepudert?

Wird dieses Lebensmittel
auf dem gleichen Grill
wie panierter/s Fisch/
Fleisch gegrillt?

Wird dieses Lebensmittel
in Erdnussöl gebraten?

**Clarification Points**

What type of garnishes are included in this dish?

What type of oil is used in the kitchen?

Is this food fried in the same fryer as items fried with breading?

Please ask the chef whether the meal I have ordered is safe for me

**Klarstellungspunkte**

Welche Beilagen sind in diesem Gericht enthalten?

Welches Öl wird in Ihrer Küche verwendet?

Wird dieses Lebensmittel im gleichen Fritiergerät wie panierte Lebensmittel frittiert?

Bitte fragen Sie Ihren Koch, ob ich dieses Gericht trotz meiner Allergie bestellen kann.

# German Breakfast Phrases

The following represents relevant phrases needed to communicate special dietary considerations to chefs and servers in restaurants around the globe for breakfast and includes:

- Breakfast meal and side dish requests

- Types of egg preparation and common ingredients

- Other breakfast items

| **Egg Dishes** | **Eiergerichte** |
|---|---|
| eggs benedict | Eier Benedikt |
| huevos mexicanos | Rührei mit Tomate und Zwiebeln mexikanische Art |
| huevos rancheros | Spiegelei auf Tortilla mexikanische Art |
| skillets – american style | Bratei amerikanische Art |

| **Eggs – Made to Order** | **Eier nach Wunsch** |
|---|---|
| eggs (white and yolk) | Eier (Eiweiß und Eigelb) |
| egg beaters | Eierschaum |
| egg white | Eiweiß |
| egg yolk | Eigelb |

| **Egg Preparation** | **Eierzubereitung** |
|---|---|
| boiled | gekocht |
| fried in butter | in Butter gebraten |
| fried in oil | in Öl gebraten |
| hard boiled | hart gekocht |
| poached | pochiert |
| scrambled with milk and cooked in butter | verrührt mit Milch und in Butter gebacken |
| scrambled plain or with water and cooked in oil | verrührt natur oder mit Wasser und in Öl gebacken |

| **Egg Preparation** | **Eierzubereitung** |
| --- | --- |
| soft boiled | weich gekocht |
| sunny side up | Spiegelei |
| yolk broken | verrührtes Eigelb |

| **Omelets and Potential Ingredients** | **Omeletts und mögliche Zutaten** |
| --- | --- |
| Plain | natur |
| Asparagus | Spargel |
| Avocado | Avokado |
| bacon | Frühstücksspeck |
| broccoli | Brokkoli |
| cheese | Käse |
| chicken | Huhn |
| chiles | Chili |
| chives | Schnittlauch |
| chorizo | Chorizo |
| garlic | Knoblauch |
| green beans | grüne Bohnen |
| green pepper | grüner Paprika |
| ham | Kochschinken |
| herbs | Kräuter |
| jalapenos | Peperoni |
| mushrooms | Champignons |
| olives | Oliven |
| onions | Zwiebeln |
| potatoes | Kartoffeln |

| Omelets and Potential Ingredients | Omeletts und mögliche Zutaten |
| --- | --- |
| red peppers | roter Paprika |
| sausage – chicken | Hühnerwurst |
| sausage – pork | Schweinswurst |
| sausage – turkey | Truthahnwurst |
| spinach | Spinat |
| tomatoes | Tomaten |

| Cheese and Yogurts | Käse und Joghurts |
| --- | --- |
| cheese | Käse |
| cottage cheese | Hüttenkäse |
| plain yogurt | Naturjoghurt |
| fruit yogurt | Fruchtjoghurt |
| natural yogurt | Naturjoghurt |
| soy yogurt | Sojamilchjoghurt |
| soy fruit yogurt | Sojamilch-Fruchtjoghurt |
| yogurt drink | Joghurtgetränk |

| Meat Side Dishes | Fleischbeilagen |
| --- | --- |
| bacon | Frühstücksspeck |
| canadian bacon | Kanadischer Schinken |
| chorizo | Chorizo |
| corned beef hash | Bratkartoffeln |
| ham | Kochschinken |
| sausage – chicken | Hühnerwurst |
| sausage – pork | Schweinswurst |

**Meat Side Dishes**

sausage – turkey
steak
turkey

**Fleischbeilagen**

Truthahnwurst
Steak
Truthahn

**From the Sea Side Dishes**

lox or smoked salmon
sardines
shrimp
tuna
white fish

**Fisch und Meeresfrüchte**

Räucherlachs
Sardinen
Shrimp
Tunfisch
Weißfisch

**Potato & Salad Side Dishes**

french fries
hash browns
sauteed potatoes
mixed green salad
fruit salad

**Kartoffeln und Salate**

Pommes Frites
Bratkartoffeln
sautierte Kartoffeln
gemischter grüner Salat
Obstsalat

**Fruits**

apple
apricot
banana
berries
blueberries
blackberries

**Obst**

Apfel
Aprikose
Banane
Beeren
Heidelbeeren
Brombeeren

| Fruits | Obst |
| --- | --- |
| boysenberries | Boysen-Beeren |
| cantaloupe | Zuckermelone |
| cherries | Kirschen |
| clementines | Clementinen |
| cranberries | Preiselbeeren |
| grapes | Trauben |
| grapefruit | Grapefruit |
| honey dew | Honigmelone |
| kumquat | Kumquat |
| loganberries | Loganbeeren |
| melon | Melone |
| nectarine | Nektarine |
| orange | Orange |
| papaya | Papaya |
| peach | Pfirsich |
| pear | Birne |
| plantain | Gemüsebanane |
| pineapple | Ananas |
| plum | Pflaume |
| prunes | Zwetschge |
| raisins | Rosinen |
| raspberries | Himbeeren |
| strawberries | Erdbeeren |
| tangerine | Mandarine |

## Spreads, Jams and Jellies

butter
confiture
cream cheese
honey
jams
jellies
margarine
marmalades
peanut butter
preserves

## Aufstriche, Marmeladen und Gelees

Butter
Konfitüre
Frischkäse
Honig
Marmeladen
Gelees
Margarine
Orangenmarmeladen
Erdnussbutter
Konfitüren

## Breakfast Specialties

blintzes
cereal – cold
cereal – hot
crepes
french toast
pancakes
waffles
toast

## Frühstücksspezialitäten

Blintzen
Getreideflocken – kalt
Getreideflocken – warm
Crêpe
arme Ritter
Pfannenkuchen
Waffeln
Toast

| Bakery Products | Backwaren |
|---|---|
| bagels | Bagels |
| biscuits | weiches Brötchen |
| breads | Brote |
| bunssüßes | Brötchen |
| coffee cake | Kaffeekuchen |
| crackers | Cracker |
| croissant | Croissant |
| donuts | Berliner |
| muffin | Muffin |
| rolls | Brötchen |
| rice cakes | Reiskuchen |
| scones | schottisches Teegebäck |

| Acceptable Gluten-Free Grains | Zulässige glutenfreie Körner |
|---|---|
| amaranth | Fuchsschwanz |
| buckwheat | Buchweizen |
| corn | Mais |
| millet | Hirse |
| quinoa | Reismelde |
| rice | Reis |

# German Health and Product Phrases

The following represents relevant phrases needed to communicate special health considerations to medical professionals and hospitality staff while traveling around the globe. The health phrases include:

- Listing of health facilities

- Listing of health professionals

- Symptoms that may need to be communicated to medical professionals

- Helpful products

## Health and Store Facilities

I'm looking for/ need a:
  drug store
  health food store
  grocery store
  hospital
  pharmacy

## Medizinische Einrichtung und Läden

Ich suche nach einer/einem:
  Drogerie
  Reformhaus
  Lebensmittelgeschäft
  Krankenhaus
  Apotheke

| Health Professionals | Auf medizinischem Gebiet tätige Personen |
|---|---|
| I need to see/speak with a: | Ich brauche/möchte zu einem: |
| doctor | Arzt |
| dietician | Diätassistenten/ Ernährungswissen- schaftler |
| nutritionist | Diätetiker/ Ernährungsberater |
| pediatrician | Kinderarzt |
| pharmacist | Apotheker |

| Symptoms | Symptome |
|---|---|
| I have severe/moderate: | Ich habe starke/n/s - mittlere/n/s: |
| abdominal bloating | Blähungen |
| abdominal cramping | Bauchkrämpfe |
| acid reflux | Sodbrennen |
| asthma | Asthma |
| bone/ joint pain | Knochen-/ Gelenkschmerzen |
| constipation | Verstopfung |
| diarrhea | Durchfall |
| eczema | Ekzeme |

## Symptoms

fatigue

flatulence (gas)

headaches
hives
migraines
mouth ulcers
nausea
rash
seizures
sinus infection
vomiting
wheezing

## Symptome

Ermüdungserschei
    nungen

Flatulenz
    (Darmgasbildung)

Kopfschmerzen
Nesselsucht
Migräne
Mundgeschwüre
Übelkeit
Hautausschlag
Anfälle
Stirnhöhleninfektion
Erbrechen
keuchende Atmung

## Allergen Free Products

I would like to purchase
products that are:
    organic
    corn-free
    dairy-free
    egg-free
    fish-free
    gluten-free
    milk-free

## Allergenfreie Produkte

Ich möchte Produkte
kaufen, die Folgendes sind:
    organisch
    maisfrei
    ohne Milchprodukte
    ohne Ei
    ohne Fisch
    glutenfrei
    milchfrei

### Allergen Free Products
nut-free
peanut-free
shellfish-free
soy-free
wheat-free

### Allergenfreie Produkte
ohne Nüsse
ohne Erdnüsse
ohne Schalentiere
ohne Soja
weizenfrei

### Beverages
Do you have:
gingerale
chamomile tea
detox tea
ginger tea
green tea
peppermint tea

### Getränke
Haben Sie:
Gingerale
Tee (Kamille)
Tee (entgiftend)
Tee (Ingwer)
Tee (grün)
Tee (Pfefferminz)

### Herbs/Supplements/Medicines

I am looking for:
acid reflux medicine

aloe vera
analgesic ointment
antacids
antihistamine
calomine lotion

### Kräuter/Nahrungsergänzungsstoffe/Medikamente

Ich suche nach:
Medizin gegen
  Sodbrennen
Aloe Vera
schmerzlindernde Salbe
Magensäuremittel
Antihistamine
Galmeilotion (Zinksalbe)

| Herbs/Supplements/Medicines | Kräuter/Nahrungsergänzungsstoffe/Medikamente |
|---|---|
| charcoal | Aktivkohle |
| dandelion root | Löwenzahnwurzel |
| digestive aids | Verdauungshilfen |
| digestive enzymes | verdauungsfördernde Enzyme |
| epinephrine | Adrenalin |
| fennel | Fenchel |
| ginger | Ingwer |
| ginger root | Ingwerwurzel |
| grapefruit seed | Grapefruitkerne |
| hydrochloric acid | Salzsäure |
| itch stopping cream | juckreizlindernde Creme |
| milk of magnesium | Magnesiamilch |
| peppermint | Pfefferminz |
| probiotics | probiotisches Mittel |
| tumeric | Kurkuma (Gelbwurz) |
| - to take orally | - zum Einnehmen |
| - to apply topically | - zum Einreiben |

## Bath

## Bad

I would like to buy:

Ich möchte Folgendes kaufen:

| | |
|---|---|
| bath salt | Badesalz |
| sea salts | Meersalz |
| epsom salts | Bittersalz |

*One of the very nicest things about life
is the way we must regularly stop whatever it is we
are doing and devote our attention to eating.*
—Luciano Pavarotti

# Italian Language Translations

## Phrase Overview

The following materials outline English to Italian translations for:

- Food allergy phrases

- Ingredient and preparation technique phrases

- Dining phrases

- Breakfast phrases

- Health and product phrases

# Italian Food Allergy Phrases

The following represents a partial list of phrases needed to communicate some allergy conditions and potential allergens including:

- General allergy conditions
- 10 common food allergens

## Allergy Conditions

I have/am experiencing:
- an emergency
- anaphylactic shock
- an allergic reaction
- food allergies
- celiac/coeliac disease
- lactose intolerance

## Stato Allergico

Soffro di/mi trovo in:
- un'emergenza
- shock anafilattico
- reazione allergica
- allergie alimentari
- celiachia
- intolleranza al lattosio

## 10 Common Allergens

I am allergic/intolerant/
hypersensitive to:
- corn
- dairy
- eggs
- fish
- gluten

## 10 Più Comuni Allergeni

Ho un'allergia/intolleranza/
ipersensibilità a:
- granturco
- latticini
- uova
- pesce
- glutine

| **10 Common Allergens** | **10 Più Comuni Allergeni** |
|---|---|
| milk | latte |
| nuts | noci |
| peanuts | arachidi |
| shellfish | crostacei |
| soy | soia |
| wheat | frumento |

# Italian Ingredient and Preparation Technique Phrases

The following represents a partial list of phrases needed to inquire about the specific cuisines and preparation considerations including:

- Key ingredients by the 10 common food allergens

- Food preparation techniques by the 10 common food allergens

- Other potential food allergens

## Key Cuisine Codes by Allergen

| **Corn** | **Granturco** |
|---|---|
| almond extract | estratto di mandorle |
| artificial bacon bits | surrogato di bacon a quadretti |

| Corn | Granturco |
|---|---|
| artificial mashed potato mix | miscela per surrogato di purè di patate |
| batter | pastella |
| bouillon | brodo di dado |
| bread or bread crumbs | pane o pangrattato |
| breading | miscela per impanare |
| cheese | formaggio |
| colors or flavors | coloranti o aromi |
| corn flour or corn meal | farina di granturco o polenta |
| corn starch | amido di granturco |
| corn syrup | sciroppo di granturco |
| vanilla extract | estratto di vaniglia |
| imitation crab meat or seafood | surrogato di polpa di granchio o frutti di mare |
| malt | malto |
| masa | masa |
| salad dressing | condimento per insalata |
| sauce, dipping sauce or salsa | salse (a parte e non) o salsa di pomodoro |
| seasonings | condimenti |
| side dishes or accompaniments | contorni (a parte e non) |
| tortillas or tortilla chips | tortillas o tortilla chips |
| vegetable oil | olio vegetale |

## Dairy

| | |
|---|---|
| artificial mashed potato mix | miscela per surrogato di purè di patate |
| bread or bread crumbs | pane o pangrattato |
| breading | miscela per impanare |
| butter | burro |
| cakes or cookies | torte o biscotti |
| cheese or blue cheese | formaggio o gorgonzola |
| chocolate | cioccolato |
| colors or flavors | coloranti o aromi |
| cream, sour cream or whipped cream | panna, panna acida o panna montata |
| milk or buttermilk | latte o latticello |
| sauce or dipping sauce | salse (a parte e non) |
| seasonings | condimenti |
| side dishes or accompaniments | contorni (a parte e non) |
| yogurt, yogurt curd or yogurt sauce | yogurt, crema di yogurt o salsa di yogurt |

## Latticini

## Eggs

| | |
|---|---|
| batter | pastella |
| bread or bread crumbs | pane o pangrattato |
| breading | miscela per impanare |
| cakes or cookies | torte o biscotti |
| croutons | crostini |

## Uova

## Eggs

custard
dumpling skin
egg sealer
egg yolk
imitation crab meat
    or seafood
mayonnaise
noodles or pasta
salad dressing
sauce or dipping sauce
side dishes or
    accompaniments

## Uova

crema pasticcera
pasta per ravioli al vapore
albume da pennellare
tuorlo
surrogato di polpa di
    granchio o frutti di mare
maionese
vermicelli o pasta
condimento per insalata
salse (a parte e non)
contorni (a parte e non)

## Fish

anchovies
fish sauce
imitation crab meat
    or seafood
salad dressing
salmon
stock or broth
tuna

## Pesce

acciughe
salsa di pesce
surrogato di polpa di
    granchio o frutti di mare
condimento per insalata
salmone
brodo
tonno

| **Gluten/Wheat** | **Glutine/Frumento** |
|---|---|
| artificial bacon bits | surrogato di bacon a quadretti |
| artificial mashed potato mix | miscela per surrogato di purè di patate |
| batter | pastella |
| beans | fagioli |
| bouillon | brodo di dado |
| bread or bread crumbs | pane o pangrattato |
| breading | miscela per impanare |
| cakes or cookies | torte o biscotti |
| cheese or blue cheese | formaggio o gorgonzola |
| colors or flavors | coloranti o aromi |
| croutons | crostini |
| dedicated fryer | friggitrice dedicata |
| dumpling skin | pasta per ravioli al vapore |
| fish sauce | salsa di pesce |
| flour dusting | infarinatura |
| fluffing agent | agente lievitante |
| fresh oil | olio di oliva |
| imitation crab meat or seafood | surrogato di polpa di granchio o frutti di mare |
| malt | malto |
| malt vinegar | aceto di malto |
| marinade | marinata |
| noodles or pasta | vermicelli o pasta |

## Gluten/Wheat

salad dressing

sauce, dipping sauce
   or salsa

seasonings

side dishes or
   accompaniments

soy sauce

stabilizers

thickening agent

tortillas or tortilla chips

wheat flour

yogurt, yogurt curd or
   yogurt sauce

## Glutine/Frumento

condimento per insalata

salse (a parte e non) o
   salsa di pomodoro

condimenti

contorni (a parte e non)

salsa di soia

stabilizzanti

addensante

tortillas o tortilla chips

farina di frumento

yogurt, crema di yogurt
   o salsa di yogurt

## Peanuts

bread or bread crumbs

cakes or cookies

colors or flavors

garnishes

peanut oil

sauce or dipping sauce

side dishes or
   accompaniments

vegetable bisque

vegetable oil

## Arachidi

pane o pangrattato

torte o biscotti

coloranti o aromi

guarnizioni

olio di arachidi

salse (a parte e non)

contorni (a parte e non)

minestra di verdure

olio vegetale

## Shellfish

calamari
crab
escargot (snails)
lobster
mussels
oysters
shrimp
stock or broth

## Soy

artificial bacon bits

artificial mashed potato
   mix
bean curd
bouillon
bread or bread crumbs
breading
cheese
chocolate
colors or flavors
imitation crab meat or
   seafood
ketchup
masa

## Molluschi/Crostacei

calamari
granchio
escargot (lumache)
aragosta
cozze
ostriche
gamberi
brodo

## Soia

surrogato di bacon a
   quadretti
miscela per surrogato di
   purè di patate
formaggio vegetale
brodo di dado
pane o pangrattato
miscela per impanare
formaggio
cioccolato
coloranti o aromi
surrogato di polpa di
   granchio o frutti di mare
ketchup
masa

## Soy

mayonnaise
salad dressing
sauce, dipping sauce or
    salsa
seasonings
side dishes or
    accompaniments
soy sauce
tofu
tortillas or tortilla chips
vegetable oil
yogurt, yogurt curd or
    yogurt sauce

## Soia

maionese
condimento per insalata
salse (a parte e non) o
    salsa di pomodoro
condimenti
contorni (a parte e non)

salsa di soia
tofu
tortillas o tortilla chips
olio vegetale
yogurt, crema di yogurt
    o salsa di yogurt

## Tree Nuts

almonds or almond
    extract
bread or bread crumbs
cakes or cookies
colors or flavors
cashews or cashew powder
garnishes
pistachios
sauce, dipping sauce or
    salsa

## Noci Varie

mandorle o estratto di
    mandorle
pane o pangrattato
torte o biscotti
coloranti o aromi
acagiù intero o in polvere
guarnizioni
pistacchi
salse (a parte e non) o
    salsa di pomodoro

## Tree Nuts

side dishes or
    accompaniments
vegetable bisque
walnuts

## Noci Varie

contorni (a parte e non)

minestra di verdure
noci

## Other Potential Food Allergens

I am allergic/intolerant/
hypersensitive to:
    aspartame
    bacon
    dyes
    fructose
    garlic
    ham
    monosodium glutamate
    onions
    pork
    preservatives
    rice
    sodium nitrate
    vegetable starch
    vinegar
    yeast

## Altri Potenziali Allergeni Alimentari

Ho un'allergia/intolleranza/
ipersensibilità a:
    aspartame
    bacon (pancetta)
    coloranti
    fruttosio
    aglio
    prosciutto
    glutammato monosodico
    cipolle
    maiale
    conservanti
    riso
    nitrato di sodio
    amido vegetale
    aceto
    lievito

# Italian Dining Phrases

The following represents relevant phrases needed to communicate special dietary considerations to chefs and servers in restaurants around the globe and include:

- Introductions and common courtesies
- Special requests to ensure safe dining
- Clarification questions to ensure against cross contamination

### Introductions

Hello. I'm sorry, but I do not speak Italian.

I need to special order my meal due to my food allergies.

I am on a medically prescribed allergy-free diet.

I need your assistance.

Thank you for your help.

I cannot eat these foods because I will become ill.

### Frasi di Circostanza

Salve. Mi dispiace, non parlo italiano.

Soffro di allergie ali mentari, quindi devo ordinare cibi particolari.

Il mio medico mi ha prescritto una dieta priva di allergeni.

Ho bisogno del suo aiuto.

Grazie per la cortesia.

Non posso mangiare questi cibi, perché potrebbero farmi stare male.

## Introductions

I have a condition called celiac/coeliac disease.

I cannot eat the smallest amount of gluten which is wheat, rye or barley.

## Foods that I can eat

I can eat:
  all kinds of fruit
  meat
  potatoes
  rice
  fresh stocks and broths
  all kinds of vegetables
  wine based vinegars
  distilled vinegar
  rice flour or gluten-free
    noodles
  sauce with butter, eggs,
    vegetables, olive oil,
    tomatoes, herbs

## Frasi di Circostanza

Soffro di un disturbo chiamato celiachia

Non posso mangiare glutine, che è contenuto nel frumento, nella segale, e nell'orzo neppure in minime quantità.

## Cibi Permessi

Posso mangiare:
  tutti i tipi di frutta
  carne
  patate
  riso
  consommè e brodo fresco
  tutti i tipi di verdure
  aceti a base di vino
  aceto distillato
  spaghetti di farina di
    riso o senza glutine
  salsa a base di burro,
    uova, verdure, olio
    d'oliva, pomodori, erbe

### Foods that I can eat

I prefer food that is:
- broiled
- grilled
- pan fried
- roasted
- steamed

Could you suggest a few menu items that are safe for me to eat with my allergies?

### Special Food Requests

Please:
- salad dressing on the side

- sauce on the side
- plain

No:
- bread
- breading
- bread crumbs
- butter
- chocolate
- corn starch
- cream

### Cibi Permessi

Preferisco i cibi:
- ai ferri
- grigliati
- fritti in padella
- arrostiti
- al vapore

Potrebbe consigliarmi dei piatti del menu adatti nonostante le mie allergie?

### Richieste Speciali

Per favore:
- condimento per l'insalata a parte
- salsa a parte
- senza condimenti

Niente:
- pane
- pan grattato
- molliche di pane
- burro
- cioccolato
- amido di granturco
- panna

| **Special Food Requests** | **Richieste Speciali** |
|---|---|
| croutons | crostini |
| ketchup | ketchup |
| mayonnaise | maionese |
| pasta | pasta |
| peanut oil | olio di arachidi |
| salad dressing | condimento per l'insalata |
| soy sauce | salsa di soia |
| vegetable oil | olio vegetale |
| corn tortilla | tortilla di granturco |
| wheat flour tortilla | tortilla di farina di frumento |

No dish with wheat flour in the:

    batter

    bouillon

    meat/fish dusting

    sauce

Nessun piatto con farina di frumento nella/nel:

    pastella

    brodo

    insaporitore per carne/pesce

    salsa

Do you have wheat free soy sauce?

Avete salsa di soia senza frumento?

### Clarification Points

If you are uncertain
about what the food
contains, please tell me.

Is this food dusted with
wheat flour prior to
cooking?

Is this food cooked on the
same grill as fish/meat
cooked with breading?

Is this food fried in
peanut oil?

What type of garnishes
included in this dish?

What type of oil is used
in the kitchen?

Is this food fried in the
same fryer as items fried
with breading?

Please ask the chef whether
the meal I have ordered is
safe for me.

### Chiarimenti

Se non sa con certezza
cosa contengono i cibi,
la prego di dirmelo.

Prima della cottura questo
cibo viene infarinato con
farina di frumento?

Questo cibo viene cotto
sulla stessa griglia su
cui vengono cotti
pesce/carni impanate?

Questo cibo viene cotto
con olio di arachidi?

Che contorni vengono are
serviti con questo piatto?

Che tipo di olio usate in
cucina?

Questo cibo viene cotto
nella stessa friggitrice
usata per i cibi?

Può chiedere allo chef
se il cibo che ho ordinato
è sicuro per me.

# Italian Breakfast Phrases

The following represents relevant phrases needed to communicate special dietary considerations to chefs and servers in restaurants around the globe for breakfast and include:

- Breakfast meal and side dish requests

- Types of egg preparation and common ingredients

- Other breakfast items

### Egg Dishes

eggs benedict
mexicano
rancheros
skilets – american style

### Piatti a Base di Uova

uova alla benedict
uova alla messicana
huevos rancheros (piccanti)
uova strapazzate
   all'americana

### Eggs – Made to Order

eggs (white and yolk)
egg beaters
egg white
egg yolk

### Uova su Ordinazione

uova (intere)
uova frullate
albume
tuorlo

### Egg Preparation

boiled
fried in butter
fried in oil
hard boiled
poached
scrambled with milk
    and cooked in butter
scrambled plain or with
    water and cooked in oil
soft boiled
sunny side up
yolk broken

### Preparazione delle Uova

bollite
fritte nel burro
fritte nell'olio
sode
in camicia
strapazzate con latte e
    cotte nel burro
strapazzate, da sole o con
    acqua, e cotte nell'olio
alla coque
al tegamino, tuorlo intero
al tegamino, tuorlo rotto

### Omelets and Potential Ingredients

plain
asparagus
avocado
bacon
broccoli
cheese
chicken
chiles
chives
chorizo
garlic

### Omelette e Possibili Ingredienti

semplici
asparagi
avocado
bacon
broccoli
formaggio
pollo
chile
erba cipollina
chorizo
aglio

## Omelets and Potential Ingredients

| | |
|---|---|
| green beans | fagiolini |
| green peppers | peperoni verdi |
| ham | prosciutto |
| herbs | erbette |
| jalapenos | peperoncini jalapenos |
| mushrooms | funghi |
| olives | olive |
| onions | cipolle |
| potatoes | patate |
| red peppers | peperoni rossi |
| sausage – chicken | salsiccia di pollo |
| sausage – pork | salsiccia di suino |
| sausage – turkey | salsiccia di tacchino |
| spinach | spinaci |
| tomatoes | pomodori |

## Omelette e Possibili Ingredienti

## Cheese and Yogurts

| | |
|---|---|
| cheese | formaggio |
| cottage cheese | ricotta |
| plain yogurt | yogurt bianco |
| fruit yogurt | yogurt alla frutta |
| natural yogurt | yogurt naturale |
| soy yogurt | yogurt di soia |
| soy fruit yogurt | yogurt di soia alla frutta |
| yogurt drink | bevanda allo yogurt |

## Formaggi e Yogurt

### Meat Side Dishes

bacon

canadian bacon

chorizo

corned beef hash

ham

sausage – chicken

sausage – pork

sausage – turkey

steak

turkey

### Secondi a Base di Carne

bacon

bacon canadese

chorizo

pasticcio di carne

prosciutto

salsiccia di pollo

salsiccia di suino

salsiccia di tacchino

bistecca

tacchino

### From the Sea Side Dishes

lox or smoked salmon

sardines

shrimp

tuna

white fish

### Secondi a Base di Pesce

salmone affumicato

sardine

gamberetti

tonno

pesce bianco

### Potato & Salad Side Dishes

french fries

hash browns

sauteed potatoes

mixed green salad

fruit salad

### Contorni a Base di Patate e Insalate

patatine fritte

patate alla piastra

patate arrosto

insalata verde mista

insalata di frutta

| Fruits | Frutta |
|--------|--------|
| **Fruits** | **Frutta** |
| apple | mela |
| apricot | albicocca |
| banana | banana |
| berries | frutti di bosco |
| blueberries | mirtilli |
| blackberries | more |
| boysenberries | more rosse |
| cantaloupe | cantalupo |
| cherries | ciliege |
| clementines | clementine |
| cranberries | ribes |
| grapes | uva |
| grapefruit | pompelmo |
| honey dew | melata |
| kumquat | kumquat |
| loganberries | bacche |
| melon | melone |
| nectarine | nettarina |
| orange | arancia |
| papaya | papaya |
| peach | pesca |
| pear | pera |
| plantain | plantano |
| pineapple | ananas |
| plum | susina |

| Fruits | Frutta |
|---|---|
| prunes | prugne secche |
| raisins | uva passa |
| raspberries | lamponi |
| strawberries | fragole |
| tangerine | mandarino |

| Spreads, Jams and Jellies | Prodotti Spalmabili, Marmellate e Gelatine |
|---|---|
| butter | burro |
| confiture | confettura |
| cream cheese | formaggio spalmabile |
| honey | miele |
| jams | marmellate |
| jellies | gelatine |
| margarine | margarina |
| marmalades | marmellate d'arancia |
| peanut butter | burro d'arachidi |
| preserves | conserve |

| Bakery Products | Prodotti da Forno |
|---|---|
| bagels | ciambelline |
| biscuits | biscottini |
| breads | pane |
| buns | panini dolci |
| coffee cake | torta al caffè |

## Bakery Products

crackers
croissant
donuts
muffin
rolls
rice cakes
scones

## Prodotti da Forno

cracker
croissant
krapfen
muffin
panini
gallette di riso
bollos escocés

## Breakfast Specialties

blintzes
cereal – cold
cereal – hot
crepes
french toast
pancakes
waffles
toast

## Specialità per la Colazione

frittate al formaggio
cereali a freddo
cereali a caldo
crespelle
french toast
frittelle
cialde
toast

## Acceptable Gluten-Free Grains

amaranth
buckwheat
corn
millet
quinoa
rice

## Granaglie Approvate da Gluten Free

amaranto
grano saraceno
granturco
miglio
quinoa
riso

# Italian Health and Product Phrases

The following represents relevant phrases needed to communicate special health considerations to medical professionals and hospitality staff while traveling around the globe. The health phrases include:

- Listing of health facilities

- Listing of health professionals

- Symptoms that may need to be communicated to medical professionals

- Helpful products

| Health and Store Facilities | Strutture Sanitarie e Negozi |
|---|---|
| I'm looking for/ need a: | Sto cercando/mi serve un/una: |
| drug store | negozio di generi vari (parafarmaceutici) |
| health food store | negozio di prodotti biologici |
| grocery store | drogheria |
| hospital | ospedale |
| pharmacy | farmacia |

## Health Professionals

I need to see/speak
with a:

  doctor
  dietician
  nutritionist
  pediatrician
  pharmacist

## Symptoms

I have severe/moderate:


  abdominal bloating
  abdominal cramping
  acid reflux
  asthma
  bone/ joint pain
  constipation
  diarrhea
  eczema
  fatigue
  flatulence (gas)
  headaches
  hives
  migraines
  mouth ulcers

## Personale Sanitario

Devo vedere/parlare
con un:

  medico
  dietologo
  nutrizionista
  pediatra
  farmacista

## Sintomi

Soffro in modo grave/
leggero di:

  gonfiore addominale
  crampi addominali
  riflusso acido
  asma
  dolori alle ossa/giunture
  stipsi
  diarrea
  eczema
  affaticamento
  flatulenza (gas)
  mal di testa
  orticaria
  emicranie
  ulcere della bocca

| Symptoms | Sintomi |
|---|---|
| nausea | nausea |
| rash | rash cutaneo |
| seizures | attacchi |
| sinus infection | sinusite |
| vomiting | vomito |
| wheezing | affanno |

**Allergen Free Products**

I would like to purchase products that are:

organic

corn-free

dairy-free

egg-free

fish-free

gluten-free

milk-free

nut-free

**Prodotti Privi di Allergeni**

Vorrei acquistare prodotti:

biologici

che non contengano granturco

che non contengano latticini

che non contengano uova

che non contengano pesce

che non contengano glutine

che non contengano latte

che non contengano noci

| **Allergen Free Products** | **Prodotti Privi di Allergeni** |
|---|---|
| peanut-free | che non contengano arachidi |
| shellfish-free | che non contengano crostacei |
| soy-free | che non contengano soia |
| wheat-free | che non contengano frumento |

| **Beverages** | **Bevande** |
|---|---|
| Do you have: | Avete: |
| gingerale | gingerale (bevanda allo zenzero) |
| chamomile tea without caffeine | camomilla |
| detox tea without caffeine | tisana disintossicante |
| ginger tea with caffeine | tè allo zenzero |
| ginger tea without caffeine | tisana allo zenzero |
| green tea | té verde |
| peppermint tea with caffeine | té alla menta |
| peppermint tea without caffeine | tisana alla menta |

## Herbs/Supplements/Medicines

## Erbe/Integratori/Medicinali

I am looking for:

Avrei bisogno di:

| | |
|---|---|
| acid reflux medicine | medicinale antiriflusso |
| aloe vera | aloe vera |
| analgesic ointment | pomata analgesica |
| antacids | antiacidi |
| antihistamine | antistaminici |
| calomine lotion | lozione alla calamina |
| charcoal | carbone |
| dandelion root | radice di dente di leone |
| digestive aids | prodotti che favoriscono la digestione |
| digestive enzymes | enzimi che favoriscono la digestione |
| epinephrine | epinefrina |
| fennel | finocchio |
| ginger | zenzero |
| ginger root | radice di zenzero |
| grapefruit seed | semi di pompelmo |
| hydrochloric acid | acido cloridrico |
| itch stopping cream | crema antiprurito |
| milk of magnesium | sale di magnesio |
| peppermint | menta piperita |
| probiotics | probiotici |
| tumeric | tumeric |

## Herbs/Supplements/Medicines

-to take orally
-to apply topically

## Bath

I would like to buy:
    bath salt
    sea salts
    epsom salts

## Erbe/Integratori/Medicinali

-per via orale
-per applicazione topica

## Bagno

Vorrei acquistare:
    sali da bagno
    sali marini
    sale inglese

*Conversation is food for the soul.*
—Mexican proverb

# Spanish Language Translations

## Phrase Overview

The following materials outline English to Spanish translations for:

- Food allergy phrases

- Ingredient and preparation technique phrases

- Dining phrases

- Breakfast phrases

- Health and product phrases

# Spanish Food Allergy Phrases

The following represents a partial list of phrases needed to communicate some allergy conditions and potential allergens including:

- General allergy conditions
- 10 common food allergens

## Allergy Conditions

I have/am experiencing:
- an emergency
- anaphylactic shock
- an allergic reaction
- food allergies
- celiac/coeliac disease
- lactose intolerance

## Problemas Alérgicos

Estoy experimentando:
- una emergencia
- un choque anafiláctico
- una reacción alérgica
- alergia a los alimentos
- una enfermedad celíaca
- intolerancia a la lactosa

## 10 Common Allergens

I am allergic/intolerant/hypersensitive to:
- corn
- dairy
- eggs
- fish
- gluten

## 10 Alérgenos Comunes

Soy alérgico o hipersensible:
- al maíz
- a los productos lácteos
- a los huevos
- al pescado
- al gluten

| **10 Common Allergens** | **10 Alérgenos Comunes** |
|---|---|
| milk | a la leche |
| nuts | a las nueces |
| peanuts | al cacahuates/maníes |
| shellfish | a los mariscos |
| soy | a la soya |
| wheat | al trigo |

# Spanish Ingredient and Preparation Technique Phrases

The following represents a partial listing of phrases needed to inquire about the specific cuisines and preparation considerations including:

- Key ingredients by the 10 common food allergens

- Food preparation techniques by the 10 common food allergens

- Other potential food allergens

## Key Cuisine Codes by Allergen

| **Corn** | **Maíz** |
|---|---|
| almond extract | extracto de almendra |
| artificial bacon bits | trocitos de tocino artificial |

| Corn | Maíz |
|---|---|
| artificial mashed potato mix | mezcla artificial para puré de papa |
| batter | pasta culinaria |
| bouillon | caldo |
| bread or bread crumbs | pan o trozos de pan |
| breading | miga de pan |
| cheese | queso |
| colors or flavors | colores o sabores |
| corn flour or corn meal | harina o fécula de maíz |
| corn starch | fécula de maíz |
| corn syrup | jarabe de maíz |
| imitation crab meat or seafood | cangrejo o pescados y mariscos artificiales |
| malt | malta |
| masa | masa |
| salad dressing | aderezo para ensaladas |
| sauce, dipping sauce or salsa | salsas |
| seasonings | sazones |
| side dishes or accompaniments | platos adicionales o acompañamientos |
| tortillas or tortilla chips | tortillas o trocitos de tortilla |
| vanilla extract | extracto de vainilla |
| vegetable oil | aceite vegetal |

## Dairy

artificial mashed potato
   mix

bread or bread crumbs

breading

butter

cakes or cookies

cheese or blue cheese

chocolate

colors or flavors

cream, sour cream
   or whipped cream

milk or buttermilk

sauce or dipping sauce

seasonings

side dishes or
   accompaniments

yogurt, yogurt curd
   or yogurt sauce

## Eggs

batter

bread or bread crumbs

breading

cakes or cookies

croutons

## Productos Lácteos

mezcla artificial para puré
   de papa

pan o trocitos de pan

miga de pan

mantequilla

tortas o galletas dulces

queso o queso azul

chocolate

colores o sabores

crema, crema agria o
   crema batida

leche o suero de leche

salsas

sazones

platos adicionales o
   acompañamientos

yogur, requesón de
   yogur o salsa de yogur

## Huevos

pasta culinaria

pan o trozos de pan

miga de pan

tortas o galletas dulces

trocitos de pan

## Eggs

custard
dumpling skin
egg sealer
egg yolk
imitation crab meat
    or seafood
mayonnaise
noodles or pasta
salad dressing
sauce or dipping sauce
side dishes or
    accompaniments

## Fish

anchovies
fish sauce
imitation crab meat or
    seafood
salad dressing
salmon
stock or broth
tuna

## Huevos

natillas
pasta de pudín
clara de huevo
yema de huevo
cangrejo o pescados y
    mariscos artificiales
mayonesa
fideos o pastas
aderezo para ensaladas
salsas
platos adicionales o
    acompañamientos

## Pescados

anchoas
salsa de pescado
cangrejo o pescados y
    mariscos artificiales
aderezo para ensaladas
salmón
caldos
atún

| Gluten/Wheat | Gluten/Trigo |
|---|---|
| artificial bacon bits | trocitos de tocino artificial |
| artificial mashed potato mix | mezcla artificial para puré de papa |
| batter | pasta culinaria |
| beans | granos |
| bouillon | caldo |
| bread or bread crumbs | pan o trozos de pan |
| breading | miga de pan |
| cakes or cookies | tortas o galletas dulces |
| cheese or blue cheese | queso o queso azul |
| colors or flavors | colores o sabores |
| croutons | trocitos de pan |
| dedicated fryer | ingredientes especiales para freír |
| dumpling skin | pasta de pudín |
| fish sauce | salsa de pescado |
| flour dusting | harina pulverizada |
| fluffing agent | agente para esponjar |
| fresh oil | aceite fresco |
| imitation crab meat or seafood | cangrejo o pescados y mariscos artificiales |
| malt | malta |
| malt vinegar | vinagre de malta |
| marinade | adobo |
| noodles or pasta | fideos o pastas |

### Gluten/Wheat

salad dressing
sauce, dipping sauce or salsa
seasonings
side dishes or
   accompaniments
soy sauce
stabilizers
thickening agent
tortillas or tortilla chips
wheat flour
yogurt, yogurt curd
   or yogurt sauce

### Gluten/Trigo

aderezo para ensaladas
salsas
sazones
platos adicionales o
   acompañamientos
salsa de soya
estabilizadores
agentes para espesar
tortillas o trocitos de tortilla
harina de trigo
yogur, requesón de
   yogur o salsa de yogur

### Peanuts

bread or bread crumbs
cakes or cookies
colors or flavors
garnishes
peanut oil
sauce or dipping sauce
side dishes or
   accompaniments
vegetable bisque
vegetable oil

### Cacahuates/Maníes

pan o trocitos de pan
tortas o galletas dulces
colores o sabores
adornos
aceite de maní
salsas
platos adicionales o
   acompañamientos
guisado de verduras
aceite vegetal

| **Shellfish** | **Crustáceos** |
|---|---|
| calamari | calamares |
| crab | cangrejo |
| escargot (snails) | caracoles |
| lobster | langosta |
| mussels | mejillones |
| oysters | ostras |
| mussels | mejillones |
| shrimp | camarones |
| stock or broth | caldos |

| **Soy** | **Soya** |
|---|---|
| artificial bacon bits | trocitos de tocino artificial |
| artificial mashed potato mix | mezcla artificial para puré de papa |
| bean curd | requesón de granos |
| bouillon | caldo |
| bread or bread crumbs | pan o trozos de pan |
| breading | miga de pan |
| cheese | queso |
| chocolate | chocolate |
| colors or flavors | colores o sabores |
| imitation crab meat or seafood | cangrejo o pescados y mariscos artificiales |
| ketchup | salsa de tomate |
| masa | masa |

## Soy

mayonnaise
salad dressing
sauce, dipping sauce or salsa
seasonings
side dishes or
   accompaniments
soy sauce
tofu
tortillas or tortilla chips
vegetable oil
yogurt, yogurt curd
   yogurt sauce

## Soya

mayonesa
aderezo para ensaladas
salsas
sazones
platos adicionales o
   acompañamientos
salsa de soya
queso de soya
tortillas o trocitos de tortilla
aceite vegetal
yogur, requesón de or
   yogur o salsa de yogur

## Tree Nuts

almonds or almond
   extract
bread or bread crumbs
cakes or cookies
colors or flavors
cashews or cashew powder

garnishes
pistachios
sauce, dipping sauce or salsa

## Nueces

almendras o extracto
   de almendras
pan o trozos de pan
tortas o galletas dulces
colores o sabores
marañones o polvo de
   marañón
adornos
pistachos
salsas

| ee Nuts | **Nueces** |
| --- | --- |
| de dishes or | platos adicionales o |
|   accompaniments |   acompañamientos |
| egetable bisque | guisado de verduras |
| alnuts | nueces |

| **ther Potential Food Allergens** | **Otros Alérgenos Potenciales de los Alimentos** |
| --- | --- |
| am allergic/intolerant/ | Soy alérgico, intolerante |
| ypersensitive to: | o hipersensible: |
| aspartame | al aspartamo |
| bacon | al tocino |
| dyes | a los tintes |
| fructose | a la fructosa |
| garlic | al ajo |
| ham | al jamón |
| monosodium glutamate | al glutamato sódico |
| onions | a la cebolla |
| pork | al cerdo |
| preservatives | a los preservantes |
| rice | al arroz |
| sodium nitrate | al nitrato de sodio |
| vegetable starch | al almidón vegetal |
| vinegar | al vinagre |
| yeast | a la levadura |

# Spanish Dining Phrases

The following represents relevant phrases needed to communicate special dietary considerations to chefs and servers in restaurants around the globe and include:

- Introductions and common courtesies

- Special requests to ensure safe dining

- Clarification questions to ensure against cross contamination

### Introductions

Hello. I'm sorry, but I do not speak Spanish.

I need to special order my meal due to my food allergies.

I am on a medically prescribed allergy-free diet.

I need your assistance.

Thank you for your help.

I cannot eat these foods because I will become ill.

### Introducciones

¡Hola! Lo siento, pero no hablo español.

Necesito pedir una comida especial, debido a mis alergias a los alimentos.

El médico me ha puesto a un régimen que no me cause alergias.

Necesito que me ayude.

Gracias por su ayuda.

No puedo comer estos alimentos, porque me enfermaré.

## Introductions

I have a condition called celiac/coeliac disease.

I cannot eat the smallest amount of gluten which is wheat, rye or barley.

## Foods that I can eat

I can eat:
- all kinds of fruit
- meat
- potatoes
- rice
- fresh stocks and broths
- all kinds of vegetables
- wine based vinegars
- distilled vinegar
- rice flour or gluten-free noodles
- sauce with butter, eggs, vegetables, olive oil, tomatoes, herbs

## Introducciones

Tengo un a problema, llamado "la enfermedad celíaca".

No puedo comer ni la más mínima cantidad de gluten que provenga del trigo, el centeno o la cebada.

## Alimentos que Puedo Comer

Puedo comer:
- toda clase de fruta
- carne
- patatas
- arroz
- extractos y caldos frescos
- toda clase de verduras
- vinagres de vino
- vinagre destilado
- fideos de harina de arroz o sin gluten
- salsas con mantequilla, huevos, verduras, aceite de oliva, tomates y yerbas

### Foods that I can eat

I prefer food that is:
  broiled
  grilled
  pan fried
  roasted
  steamed

Could you suggest a few
  menu items that are safe
  for me to eat with my
  allergies?

### Special Food Requests

Please:
  salad dressing on
    the side
  sauce on the side
  plain

No:
  bread
  breading
  bread crumbs
  butter
  chocolate

### Alimentos que Puedo Comer

Prefiero alimentos:
  asados al fuego
  asados a la parrilla
  fritos en sartén
  asados al horno
  al vapor

¿Podría recomendarme
  algunos platos de su
  menú, que pueda comer
  sin peligro, con mis
  alergias?

### Solicitudes Especiales

Por favor:
  el aliño de la ensalada
    aparte
  la salsa aparte
  puro, sin mezcla

Nada de:
  pan
  empanizado
  miga de pan
  mantequilla
  chocolate

| | |
|---|---|
| **Special Food Requests** | **Solicitudes Especiales** |

corn starch — fécula de maíz
cream — crema
croutons — trocitos de pan frito
ketchup — salsa de tomate
mayonnaise — mayonesa
pasta — pasta
peanut oil — aceite de cacahuate
salad dressing — aliño para la ensalada
soy sauce — salsa de soya
vegetable oil — aceite vegetal
corn tortilla — tortilla de maíz
wheat flour tortilla — tortilla de harina de trigo

**Special Food Requests**

No dish with wheat flour in the:

batter
bouillon
meat/fish dusting

sauce

Do you have wheat free soy sauce?

**Solicitudes Especiales**

Ningún ingrediente con harina de trigo:

en la pasta culinaria
en el caldo
para espolvorear la carne o el pescado
en la salsa

¿Tiene salsa de soya sin trigo?

## Clarification Points

If you are uncertain about what the food contains, please tell me.

Is this food dusted with wheat flour prior to cooking?

Is this food cooked on the same grill as fish/meat cooked with breading?

Is this food fried in peanut oil?

What type of garnishes are included in this dish?

What type of oil is used in the kitchen?

Is this food fried in the same fryer as items fried with breading?

Please ask the chef whether the meal I have ordered is safe for me

## Aclaraciones

Si tiene cualquier duda acera de lo que contienen los alimentos, por favor dígamelo.

¿Se espolvorean estos alimentos con harina de trigo, antes de cocinarlos?

¿Se cocina esta comida en la misma parrilla que la carne empanizada?

¿Se fríe esta comida en aceite de cacahuate?

¿Qué tipo de aderezos trae este plato?

¿Qué tipo de aceite se utiliza en la cocina?

¿Se fríe esta comida en la misma sartén que los platos apanados fritos?

Por favor, pregúntele al cocinero si la comida que he pedido es peligrosa para mí.

# Spanish Breakfast Phrases

The following represents relevant phrases needed to communicate special dietary considerations to chefs and servers in restaurants around the globe for breakfast and include:

- Breakfast meal and side dish requests
- Types of egg preparation and common ingredients
- Other breakfast items

| Egg Dishes | Platos de Huevo |
|---|---|
| eggs benedict | huevos benedict |
| huevos mexicanos | huevos mexicanos |
| huevos rancheros | huevos rancheros |
| skillets – american style | cacerola de huevos a la americana |

| Eggs – Made to Order | Huevos por Encargo |
|---|---|
| eggs (white and yolk) | huevos (clara y yema) |
| egg beaters | huevos revueltos |
| egg white | clara de huevo |
| egg yolk | yema de huevo |

| **Egg Preparation** | **Preparación de los Huevos** |
|---|---|
| boiled | hervidos |
| fried in butter | fritos en mantequilla |
| fried in oil | fritos en aceite |
| hard boiled | duros |
| poached | escalfados |
| scrambled with milk and cooked in butter | revueltos con leche y cocidos en mantequilla |
| scrambled plain or with water and cooked in oil | revueltos solos o con agua y cocidos en aceite |
| soft boiled | pasados por agua |
| sunny side up | fritos solamente por debajo |
| yolk broken | con la yema rota |

| **Omelets and Potential Ingredients** | **Tortillas e Ingredientes Potenciales** |
|---|---|
| plain | solamente de huevo |
| asparagus | espárragos |
| avocado | aguacate |
| bacon | tocino |
| broccoli | bróculi |
| cheese | queso |
| chicken | pollo |
| chiles | chile |
| chives | cebollanas |
| chorizo | chorizo |

| **Omelets and Potential Ingredients** | **Tortillas e Ingredientes Potenciales** |
|---|---|
| garlic | ajo |
| green beans | habichuelas verdes |
| green peppers | pimientos verdes |
| ham | jamón |
| herbs | hierbas |
| jalapenos | jalapeños |
| mushrooms | hongos |
| olives | aceitunas |
| onions | cebollas |
| potatoes | papas |
| red peppers | pimientos rojos |
| sausage – chicken | salchicha de pollo |
| sausage – pork | salchicha de cerdo |
| sausage – turkey | salchicha de pavo |
| spinach | espinaca |
| tomatoes | tomate |

| **Cheese and Yogurts** | **Quesos y Yogures** |
|---|---|
| cheese | queso |
| cottage cheese | requesón |
| plain yogurt | yogur puro |
| fruit yogurt | yogur de frutas |
| natural yogurt | yogur natural |
| soy yogurt | yogur de soya |

### Cheese and Yogurts
soy fruit yogurt
yogurt drink

### Meat Side Dishes
bacon
canadian bacon
chorizo
corned beef hash
ham
sausage – chicken
sausage – pork
sausage – turkey
steak
turkey

### From the Sea Side Dishes
lox or smoked salmon
sardines
shrimp
tuna
white fish

### Quesos y Yogures
yogur de soya con frutas
yogur líquido

### Platos de Carne Adicionales
tocino
tocino canadiense
chorizo
cecina molida
jamón
salchicha de pollo
salchicha de cerdo
salchicha de pavo
carne asada
pavo

### Pescados y Mariscos Adicionales
salmón ahumado
sardinas
camarones
atún
pescados blancos

## Potato & Salad Side Dishes

french fries

hash browns

sauteed potatoes

mixed green salad

fruit salad

## Platos Adicionales de Papa y Ensaladas

papas fritas

torta de papa picada

papas salteadas

ensalada de verduras
    mezcladas

macedonia de frutas

## Fruits

apple

apricot

banana

berries

blueberries

blackberries

boysenberries

cantaloupe

cherries

clementines

cranberries

grapes

grapefruit

honey dew

kumquat

loganberries

## Frutas

manzana

albaricoque

plátano

bayas

arándanos dulces

moras

moras y frambuesas

melón "cantaloupe"

cerezas

mandarinas

arándanos agrios

uvas

toronja

melón dulce

naranjas chinas

zarzamoras

| Fruits | Frutas |
|---|---|
| melon | melón |
| nectarine | pérsico |
| orange | naranja |
| papaya | papaya |
| peach | durazno |
| pear | pera |
| plantain | plátano verde |
| pineapple | piña |
| plum | ciruela |
| prunes | ciruelas pasas |
| raisins | uvas pasas |
| raspberries | frambuesas |
| strawberries | fresas |
| tangerine | naranja tangerina |

| Spreads, Jams and Jellies | Para Untar, Mermeladas y Jaleas |
|---|---|
| butter | mantequilla |
| confiture | compota |
| cream cheese | queso crema |
| honey | miel |
| jams | conservas |
| jellies | jaleas |
| margarine | margarina |
| marmalades | mermeladas |
| peanut butter | mantequilla de maní |
| preserves | confituras |

| Bakery Products | Productos de Panadería |
|---|---|
| bagels | "bagels" |
| biscuits | galletas |
| breads | panes |
| buns | bollos |
| coffee cake | torta de café |
| crackers | galletas saladas |
| croissant | "croissant" |
| donuts | "donuts" |
| muffin | "muffin" |
| rolls | panecillos redondos |
| rice cakes | tortitas de arroz |
| scones | panes sin leudar |

| Breakfast Specialties | Especialidades para el Desayuno |
|---|---|
| blintzes | "blintzes" |
| cereal – cold | cereal frío |
| cereal – hot | cereal caliente |
| crepes | "crepes" |
| french toast | tostada francesa |
| pancakes | "pancakes" |
| waffles | barquillos |
| toast | tostada |

| Acceptable Gluten-Free Grains | Cereales Aceptables, sin Gluten |
|---|---|
| amaranth | amaranto |
| buckwheat | alforfón |
| corn | maíz |
| millet | mijo |
| quinoa | quinua |
| rice | arroz |

# Spanish Health and Product Phrases

The following represents relevant phrases needed to communicate special health considerations to medical professionals and hospitality staff while traveling around the globe. The health phrases include:

- Listing of health facilities

- Listing of health professionals

- Symptoms that may need to be communicated to medical professionals

- Helpful products

## Health and Store Facilities

I'm looking for/need a:

    drug store

    health food store

    grocery store

    hospital

    pharmacy

## Health Professionals

I need to see/speak with a:

    doctor

    dietician

    nutritionist

    pediatrician

    pharmacist

## Centros Médicos y Tiendas de Productos Médicos

Busco o necesito:

    una droguería

    una tienda de alimentos dietéticos

    una tienda de víveres

    un hospital

    una farmacia

## Profesionales de la Salud

Necesito consultar a:
o hablar con:

    un médico

    un dietista

    un especialista en nutrición

    un pediatra

    un farmaceuta

## Symptoms

I have severe/moderate:

abdominal bloating
abdominal cramping

acid reflux
asthma
bone/ joint pain

constipation
diarrhea
eczema
fatigue
flatulence (gas)
headaches
hives
migraines
mouth ulcers
nausea
rash
seizures
sinus infection

vomiting
wheezing

## Síntomas

Tengo:...intensa(o) o
moderada(o)

distensión abdominal
contracciones dolorosas
abdominales

reflujo ácido
asma intensa
dolor en los huesos o
articulaciones

estreñimiento
diarrea
eczema
fatiga
flatulencia (gases)
dolores de cabeza
urticaria
migrañas
úlceras en la boca
náusea
erupción cutánea
convulsiones
infección de los senos
nasales

vómito
sibilancia

## Allergen Free Products

I would like to purchase
products that are:

    organic
    corn-free
    dairy-free
    egg-free
    fish-free
    gluten-free
    milk-free
    nut-free
    peanut-free
    shellfish-free
    soy-free
    wheat-free

## Productos sin Alérgenos

Me gustaría comprar
productos:

    orgánicos
    sin maíz
    no lácteos
    sin huevo
    sin pescado
    sin gluten
    sin leche
    sin nueces
    sin maní
    sin mariscos
    sin soya
    sin trigo

## Beverages

Do you have:

    gingerale
    chamomile tea
    detox tea
    ginger tea
    green tea
    peppermint tea

## Bebidas

Tiene:

    gingerale
    infusión de manzanilla
    infusión desintoxicante
    infusión de jengibre
    té verde
    infusión de hierbabuena

## Herbs/Supplements/Medicines

## Hierbas/Suplementos/Medicinas

| I am looking for: | Estoy buscando: |
|---|---|
| acid reflux medicine | una medicina para el reflujo ácido |
| aloe vera | sábila |
| analgesic ointment | un ungüento analgésico |
| antacids | antiácidos |
| antihistamine | antihistamínicos |
| calomine (sic) lotion | una loción de calamina |
| charcoal | carbón |
| dandelion root | raíz de diente de león |
| digestive aids | ayudantes de la digestión |
| digestive enzymes | enzimas digestivas |
| epinephrine | epinefrina |
| fennel | hinojo |
| ginger | jengibre |
| ginger root | raíz de jengibre |
| grapefruit seed | semilla de toronja |
| hydrochloric acid | ácido clorhídrico |
| itch stopping cream | crema para aliviar la picazón |
| milk of magnesium (sic) | leche de magnesia |
| peppermint | hierbabuena |
| probiotics | probióticos |
| tumeric (sic) | cúrcuma |

## Herbs/Supplements/Medicines

-to take orally
-to apply topically

## Bath

I would like to buy:
    bath salt
    sea salts
    epsom salts

## Hierbas/Suplementos/Medicinas

de administración oral
de aplicación tópica

## Baño

Deseo comprar:
    sales de baño
    sales marinas
    sal de epsom

# About the Authors and Additional Products

The following information highlights:

- Background of authors
- Additional books and passports

## Background of Authors

Kim Koeller has spent the last 23 years eating 80% of her meals in restaurants across the globe while managing over a dozen food-related allergies/sensitivities and celiac/coeliac disease. Robert La France has spent over twelve years in the restaurant industry and devotes his spare time to a passion for the culinary arts. Collectively,